P9-CMS-768
Gg
Hh
Ii
Jj
Kk
Ll
Mm
Uu
Ww
Xx
Yy
Zz

Dear Parent,

The My First Steps to Reading® *series is based on a teaching activity that helps children learn to recognize letters and their sounds. The use of predictable language patterns and repetition of familiar words will also help your child build a basic sight vocabulary. Your child will enjoy watching the characters in the books place imaginative objects in "letter boxes." You and your child can even create and fill your own letter box, using stuffed animals, cut-out pictures, or other objects beginning with the same letter. The things you can do together are limited only by your imagination. Learning letters will be fun—the first important step on the road to reading.*

The Editors

 Published by Scholastic Inc., 90 Old Sherman Turnpike, Danbury, Connecticut 06810, by arrangement with The Child's World, Inc.
Scholastic offers a varied selection of children's book racks and tote bags. For details about ordering, please write to: Scholastic At Home, 90 Old Sherman Turnpike, Danbury, CT 06810, Attention: Premium Department

Originally published as *My "c" Sound Box* by The Child's World, Inc.

ISBN 0-7172-6502-1

Printed in the U.S.A.

My "c" Book

(This book concentrates on the hard "c" sound in the story line. Blends are included. Words beginning with the soft "c" sound are included at the end of the book.)

written by Jane Belk Moncure
illustrated by Colin King

Little c had a box.

"I will find things that begin with my 'c' sound," she said.

"I will put them into my sound box."

Little c was cold.

She found some coats.

Little put on a coat.

Did she put the other coats into her box?

She did.

Little found some caps.

She put on a cap.

Did she put the other caps into her box with the coats? She did.

Then Little saw a caterpillar.

Before she put the caterpillar into the box, it made a

So she put the cocoon into her box.

Soon Little [girl] found a car.

She got into the car and went for a drive in the country.

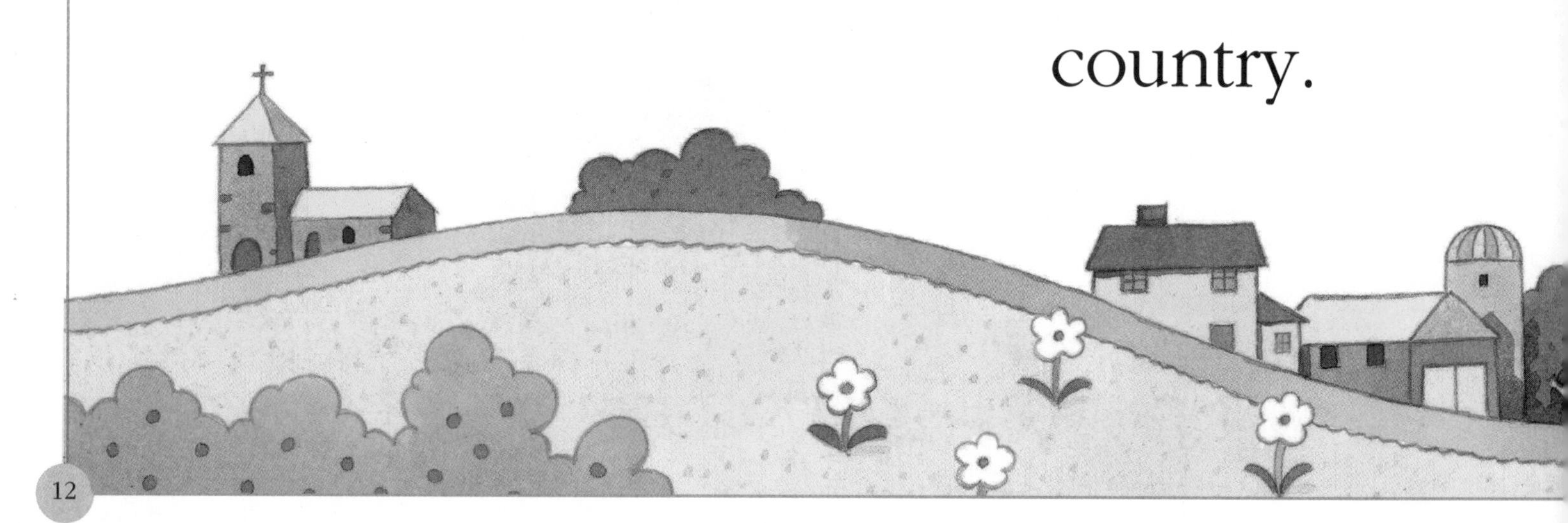

She saw a cat.

The cat was chasing a canary.

Little caught the cat.

She put it into her box.

Then she called to the canary.
The canary flew into the cage.

Little

put the cage and canary into her box.

Little saw a cow and a calf near some corn.

She put the cow, the calf, and the corn on the cob into her box. Then . . .

Little drove her car through a desert.

She saw a camel and a cactus.

She put them into her box. She drove to the end of the road, where she found . . .

a castle!

A big castle.

A clown was in the castle.

"Come in," said the clown.

Little got out of the car.

She carried her box into the castle.

She saw a
cake

with candles on it.

“You are just in time for my party!” said the clown.

Little took off her coat and cap.

She lifted the cage with
the canary out of the box.
She lifted out the cocoon
with the caterpillar inside.
Then all the other animals
came out of the box.

They all sat down
to a birthday party.

The caterpillar did not eat because it was still in the cocoon.

Can you read these words with
Little c ?
crown
can
camera
carrot
curtain
cup

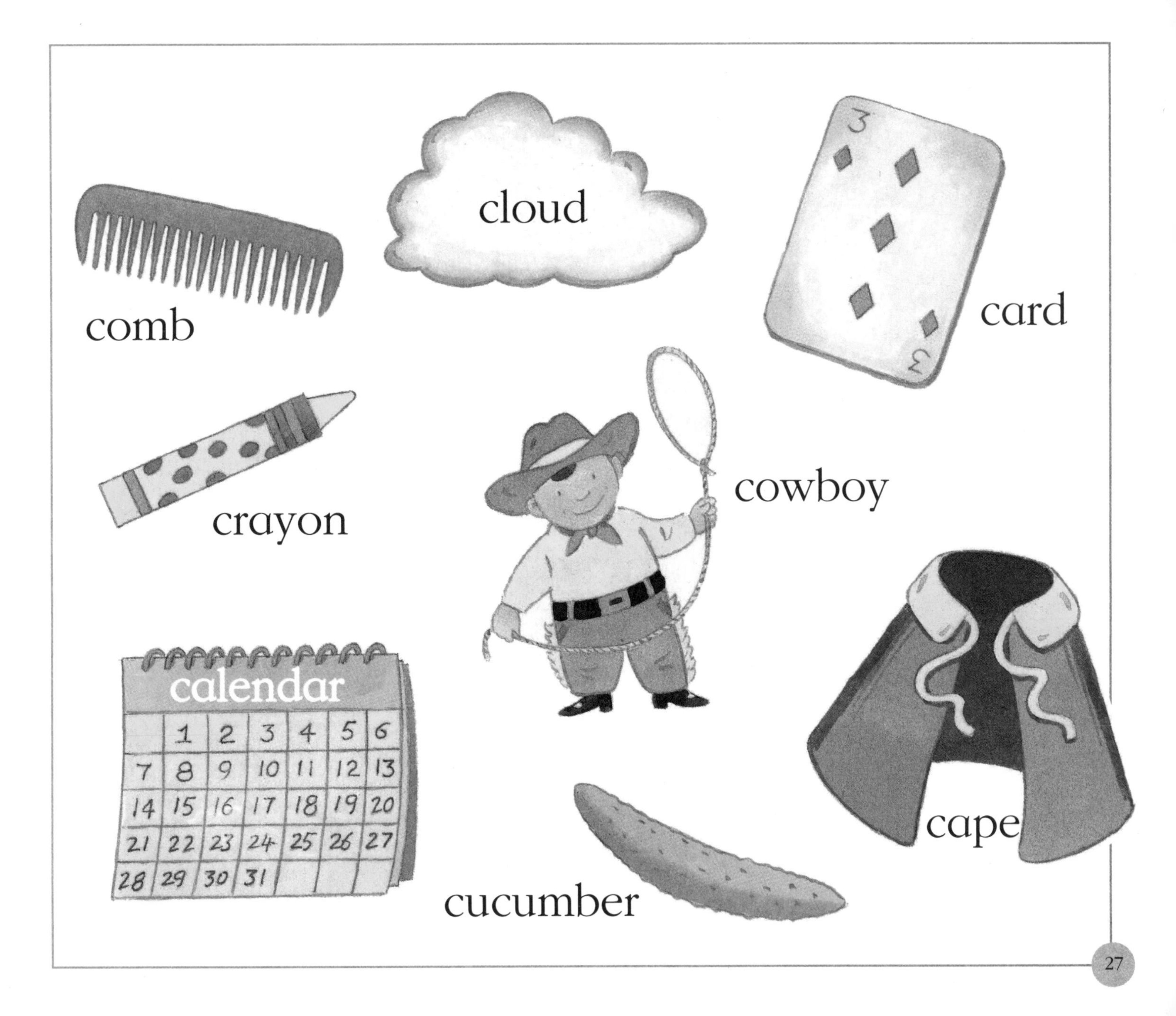

cloud
comb
card
crayon
cowboy
calendar
1 2 3 4 5 6
7 8 9 10 11 12 13
14 15 16 17 18 19 20
21 22 23 24 25 26 27
28 29 30 31
cape
cucumber

Little 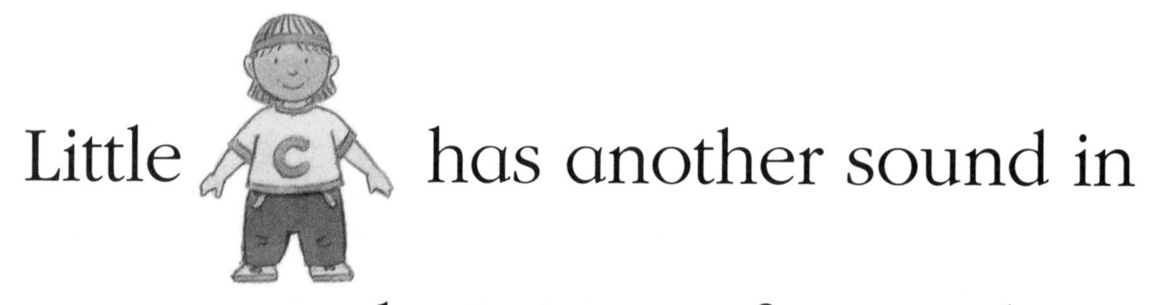 has another sound in some words. It is a soft sound.

Can you read these words?

Listen for the soft sound of Little .

circle
centipede
cymbals
celery
circus animals
cereal
city

Aa
Bb
Cc
Dd
Ee
Ff
Nn
Oo
Pp
Qq
Rr
Ss
Tt
My First Steps to READING®